Mr Toad
and other poems

Compiled by Tig Thomas

Miles Kelly

First published in 2010 by Miles Kelly Publishing Ltd
Harding's Barn, Bardfield End Green, Thaxted, Essex, CM6 3PX, UK

2 4 6 8 10 9 7 5 3 1

Editorial Director Belinda Gallagher

Art Director Jo Cowan

Assistant Editor Claire Philip

Designer Joe Jones

Junior Designer Kayleigh Allen

Production Manager Elizabeth Collins

Reprographics Stephan Davis, Ian Paulyn

ISBN 978-1-84810-392-4

Printed in China

British Library Cataloguing-in-Publication Data
A catalogue record for this book is available from the British Library

ACKNOWLEDGEMENTS

The publishers would like to thank Kirsten Wilson for
the illustrations she contributed to this book.

All other artwork from the Miles Kelly Artwork Bank

The publishers would like to thank iStockphoto.com for the use of their
photographs on pages 10 (Andreas Kaspar) and 36 (Stanislav Pobytov)

Made with paper from a sustainable forest

www.mileskelly.net
info@mileskelly.net

www.factsforprojects.com

Self-publish your
children's book

buddingpress.co.uk

Contents

Mr Toad

The world has held great Heroes,
As history-books have showed;
But never a name to go down to fame
Compared with that of Toad!

The clever men at Oxford
Know all that there is to be
    knowed.
But they none of them know
    one half as much
As intelligent Mr Toad!

The animals sat in the Ark and
    cried,
Their tears in torrents flowed.
Who was it said, "There's land ahead?"
Encouraging Mr Toad!

The army all saluted
  As they marched along the road.
    Was it the King? Or Kitchener?
      No. It was Mr Toad.

      The Queen and her Ladies-in-waiting
    Sat at the window and sewed.
  She cried, "Look! Who's that HANDSOME man?"
They answered, "Mr Toad."

Kenneth Grahame

Shall I?

"Shall I sing?" says the Lark,
"Shall I bloom?" says the Flower;
"Shall I come?" says the Sun,
"Or shall I?" says the Shower.
Sing your song, pretty Bird,
Roses, bloom for an hour;
Shine on, dearest Sun,
Go away, naughty Shower!

Kate Greenaway

What does the Bee do?

What does the bee do?
Bring home honey.
And what does Father do?
Bring home money.
And what does Mother do?
Lay out the money.
And what does baby do?
Eat up the honey.

Christina Rossetti

The Bee's Wedding

Bless you, bless you, bonny bee:
Say, when will your wedding be?
If it be tomorrow day,
Take your wings and fly away.

Anonymous

The Seasons

Spring is showery, flowery, bowery.
Summer: hoppy, croppy, poppy.
Autumn: wheezy, sneezy, freezy.
Winter: slippy, drippy, nippy.

Anonymous

The South Wind

The south wind brings wet weather;
The north wind wet and cold together;
The west wind always brings us rain;
The east wind blows it back again.

Anonymous

Pigeon's Song

Curr dhoo, curr dhoo,
Love me, and I'll love you!

Anonymous

The Quiet Snow

The quiet snow
Will splotch
Each in the row of cedars
With a fine
And patient hand;
Numb the harshness,
Tangle of that swamp.
It does not say, the sun
Does these things another way.

Even on hats of walkers,
The air of noise
And street-car ledges
It does not know
There should be hurry.

Raymond Knister

Winter

When icicles hang by the wall
And Dick the shepherd blows his nail
And Tom bears logs into the hall,
And milk comes frozen home in pail,
When blood is nipped and ways be foul,
Then nightly sings the staring owl,
Tu-who;
Tu-whit, tu-who: a merry note,
While greasy Joan doth keel the pot.
When all aloud the wind doth blow,
And coughing drowns the parson's saw,
And birds sit brooding in the snow,
And Marian's nose looks red and raw
When roasted crabs hiss in the bowl,
Then nightly sings the staring owl,
Tu-who;
Tu-whit, tu-who: a merry note,
While greasy Joan doth keel the pot.

William Shakespeare

Keel scrub
Parson's saw *the sermon*
Roasted crabs *crabapples
in a bowl of punch*

Dandelion

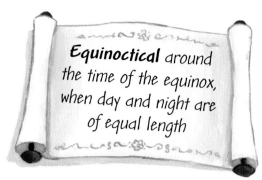

"At my time of life," said the Dandelion,
  "I keep an eye on
The slightest sign of disturbance and riot,
For my one object is to keep quiet
The reason I take such very great care,"
The old Dandy went on, "is because of my hair.
It was very thick once, and as yellow as gold;
   But now I am old,
   It is snowy-white,
   And comes off with the slightest fright.
   As to using a brush
   My good dog! I beseech you, don't rush,
   Go quietly by me, if you please
   You're as bad as a breeze.
I hope you'll attend to what we've said;
And – whatever you do – don't touch my head,
In this equinoctial, blustering weather
You might knock it off with a feather."

Juliana Horatia Ewing

The Dandelion

O dandelion, rich and haughty,
King of village flowers!
Each day is coronation time,
You have no humble hours.
I like to see you bring a troop
To beat the blue-grass spears,
To scorn the lawn-mower that would be
Like fate's triumphant shears,
Your yellow heads are cut away,
It seems your reign is o'er.
By noon you raise a sea of stars
More golden than before.

Vachel Lindsay

The Wind has such a Rainy Sound

The wind has such a rainy sound,
Moaning through the town,
The sea has such a windy sound,
Will the ships go down?
The apples in the orchard
Tumble from their tree.
Oh will the ships go down, go down,
In the windy sea?

Christina Rossetti

Blow, Wind, Blow

Blow, wind, blow! And go, mill, go!
That the miller may grind his corn;
That the baker may take it,
And into bread make it,
And bring us a loaf in the morn.

Anonymous

Rain

The rain is raining all around;
It falls on field and tree,
It rains on the umbrella here,
And on the ships at sea.

Robert Louis Stevenson

The Sea

Behold the wonders
of the deep,
Where crabs and lobsters
learn to creep,
And little fishes
learn to swim,
And clumsy sailors
tumble in.

Anonymous

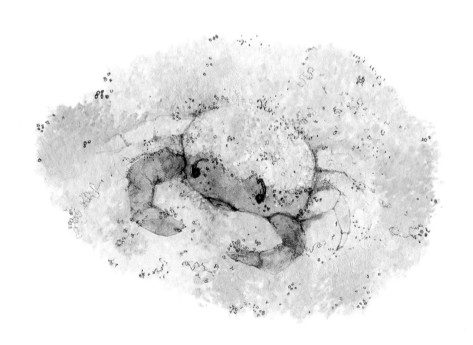

I am his Highness' Dog

I am his Highness' dog at Kew;
Pray tell me sir, whose dog
    are you?

Alexander Pope

Alexander Pope, wrote this poem when the Prince Regent, son of King George III, asked him for a poem for his dog's collar.

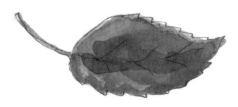

An Autumn Greeting

"Come," said the Wind to the Leaves one day.
"Come over the meadow and we will play.
Put on your dresses of red and gold.
For summer is gone and the days grow cold."

Anonymous

From **No**

No sun – no moon!
No morn – no noon –
No dawn – no dusk – no proper time of day.
No warmth, no cheerfulness, no healthful ease,
No comfortable feel in any member –
No shade, no shine, no butterflies, no bees,
No fruits, no flowers, no leaves, no birds! –
No-vember!

Thomas Hood

Member any body part

November Night

Listen. . .
With faint dry sound,
Like steps of passing ghosts,
The leaves, frost-crisp'd, break from the trees
And fall.

Adelaide Crapsey

The Duel

The gingham dog and the calico cat
Side by side on the table sat;
'Twas half-past twelve, and (what do you think!)
Nor one nor t'other had slept a wink!
The old Dutch clock and the Chinese plate
Appeared to know as sure as fate
There was going to be a terrible spat.
(I wasn't there; I simply state
What was told to me by the Chinese plate!)

The gingham dog went

"BOW-WOW-WOW!"

And the calico cat replied

"Mee-ow!"

The air was littered, an hour or so,
With bits of gingham and calico,
While the old Dutch clock in the
    chimney place
Up with its hands before its face,
For it always dreaded a family row!
(Now mind: I'm only telling you
What the old Dutch clock declares is true!)

Gingham and calico are
two sorts of material.
The gingham dog and the
calico cat are stuffed toys.

The Chinese plate looked very blue,
And wailed, "Oh, dear! What shall we do!"
But the gingham dog and the calico cat
Wallowed this way and tumbled that,
Employing every tooth and claw
In the awfullest way you ever saw –
And, oh! How the gingham and calico flew!
(Don't fancy I exaggerate –
I got my news from the Chinese plate!)

Next morning, where the two had sat
They found no trace of dog or cat;
And some folks think unto
    this day
That burglars stole that pair
    away!
But the truth about the cat and pup
Is this – they ate each other up!

"Mee-ow!"

Now what do you really think of that!
(The old Dutch clock it told me so,
And that is how I came to know.)

Eugene Field

Moon, so Round and Yellow

Moon, so round and yellow,
Looking from on high,
How I love to see you
Shining in the sky!

Oft and oft I wonder,
When I see you there,
How they get to light you,
Hanging in the air.

Where you go at morning,
When the night is past,
And the sun comes peeping
O'er the hills at last.

Sometime I will watch you
Slyly overhead,
When you think I'm sleeping
Snugly in my bed.

Matthias Barr

From *The Stars*

Look at the stars! Look, look up at the skies!
O look at all the fire-folk sitting in the air!
The bright boroughs, the circle-citadels there!
Down in dim woods the diamond
delves! the elves'-eyes!
The grey lawns cold where gold, where
quickgold lies!

Gerard Manley Hopkins

The Donkey

I saw a donkey one day old,
His head was too big
for his neck to hold;
His legs were shaky
and long and loose,
They rocked and staggered
and weren't much use.

He tried to gambol
and frisk a bit,
but he wasn't quite sure
of the trick of it.
His queer little coat
was soft and grey
and curled at his neck
in a lovely way.

His face was wistful
and left no doubt
that he felt life needed
some thinking about.
So he blundered round
in venturesome quest,
and then lay flat on the ground to rest.

He looked so little
and weak and slim,
I prayed the world
might be good to him.

Anonymous

Growing Up

Little Tommy Tadpole began to weep and wail,
    For little Tommy Tadpole had lost his little tail;
And his mother didn't know him as he wept upon a log,
    For he wasn't Tommy Tadpole,
        but Mr Thomas Frog.

Anonymous

The Robin

When father takes his spade to dig,
Then Robin comes along.
He sits upon a little twig
And sings a little song.

Or, if the trees are rather far,
He does not stay alone,
But comes up close to where we are
And bobs upon a stone.

Laurence Alma-Tadema

The Snail

The Snail he lives in his hard round house,
In the orchard, under the tree:
Says he, "I have but a single room;
But it's large enough for me."

The snail in his little house doth dwell
All the week from end to end,
You're at home, Master Snail; that's all very well.
But you never receive a friend.

Anonymous

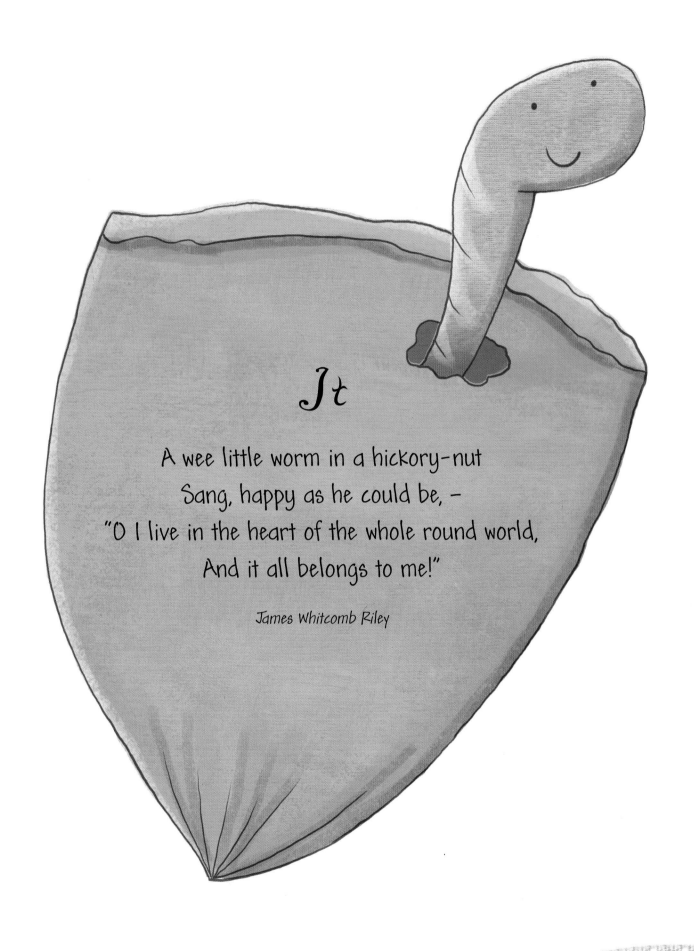

It

A wee little worm in a hickory-nut
Sang, happy as he could be, –
"O I live in the heart of the whole round world,
And it all belongs to me!"

James Whitcomb Riley

Riddle: *I have only One Foot*

I have only one foot, but thousands of toes;
My one foot stands well, but never goes;
I've a good many arms, if you count them all,
But hundreds of fingers, large and small;
From the ends of my fingers my beauty grows;
I breathe with my hair, and I drink with my toes;
I grow bigger and bigger about the waist
Although I am always very tight laced;
None e'er saw me eat – I've no mouth to bite!
Yet I eat all day, and digest all night.

In the summer, with song I shake and quiver,
But in winter I fast and groan and shiver.

George Macdonald

Answer : a tree

Escape at Bedtime

The lights from the parlour and kitchen shone out
Through the blinds and the windows and bars;
And high overhead and all moving about,
There were thousands of millions of stars.
There ne'er were such thousands of leaves on a tree,
Nor of people in church or the Park,
As the crowds of the stars that looked down upon me,
And that glittered and winked in the dark.

The Dog, and the Plough, and the Hunter, and all,
And the star of the sailor, and Mars,
These shown in the sky, and the pail by the wall
Would be half full of water and stars.
They saw me at last, and they chased me with cries,
And they soon had me packed into bed;
But the glory kept shining and bright in my eyes,
And the stars going round in my head.

Robert Louis Stevenson

The Dog, the Plough and the Hunter are patterns of stars in the sky, called constellations.

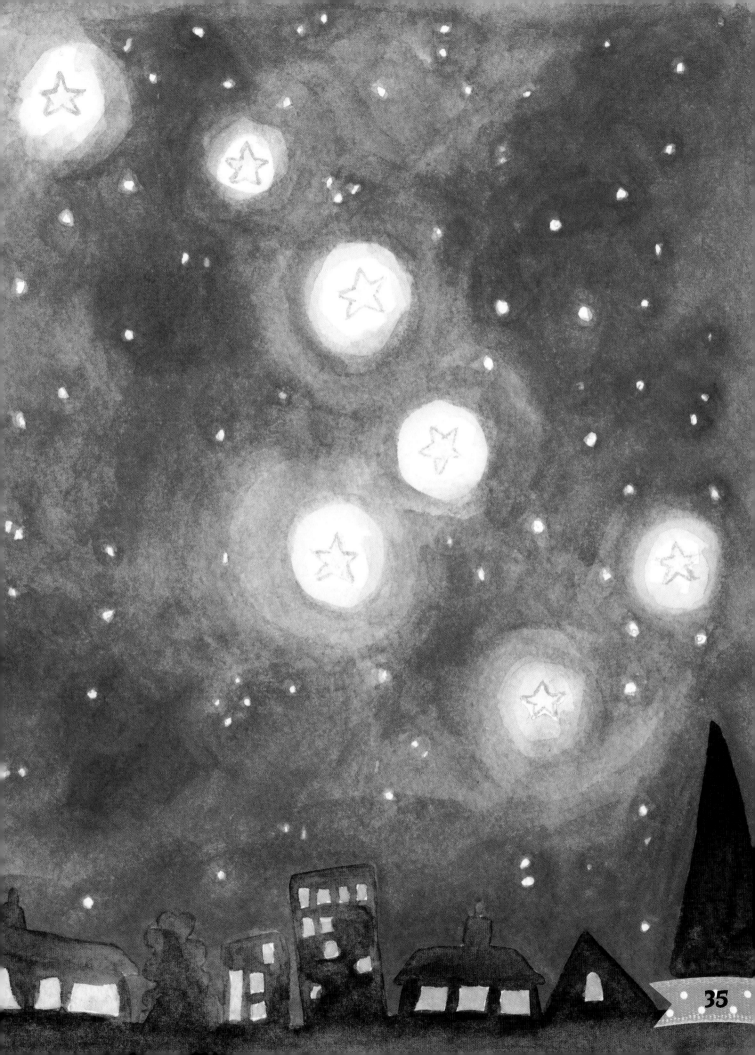

Snow

In the gloom of whiteness,
In the great silence of snow,
A child was sighing
And bitterly saying: "Oh,
They have killed a white bird up there on her nest,
The down is fluttering from her breast!"
And still it fell through that dusky brightness
On the child crying for the bird of the snow.

Edward Thomas

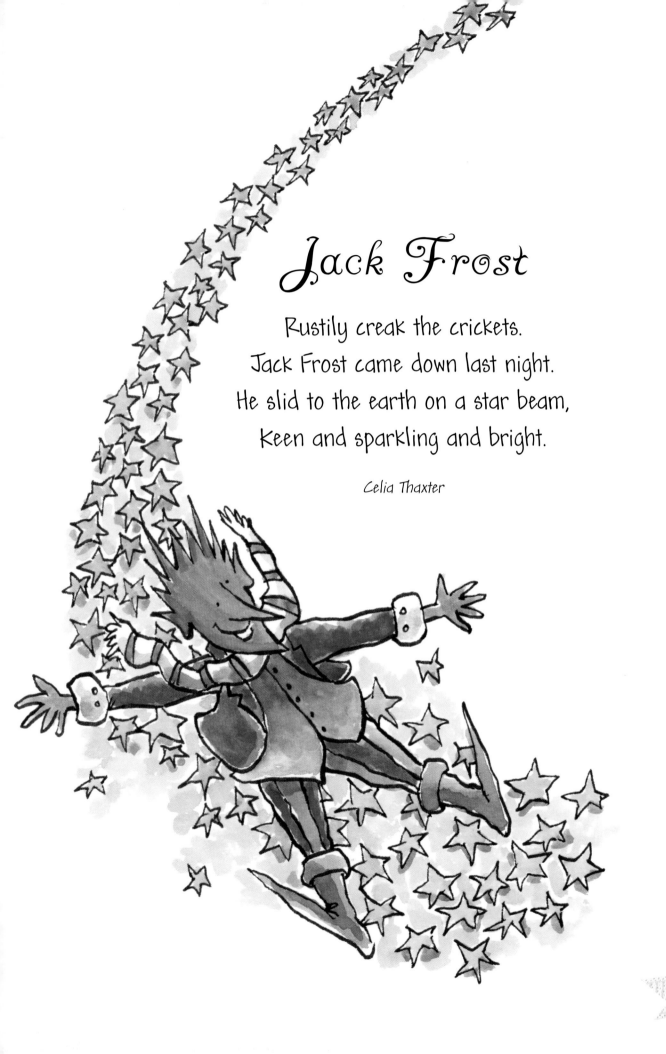

Jack Frost

Rustily creak the crickets.
Jack Frost came down last night.
He slid to the earth on a star beam,
Keen and sparkling and bright.

Celia Thaxter

The Wonderful World

Great, wide, beautiful, wonderful World,
With the wonderful water round you curled,
And the wonderful grass upon your breast,
World, you are beautifully dressed.

The wonderful air is over me,
And the wonderful wind is shaking the tree,
It walks on the water, and whirls the mills,
And talks to itself on the top of the hills.

You friendly Earth, how far do you go,
With the wheat fields that nod and the rivers that flow,
With cities and gardens and cliffs and isles,
And the people upon you for thousands of miles?

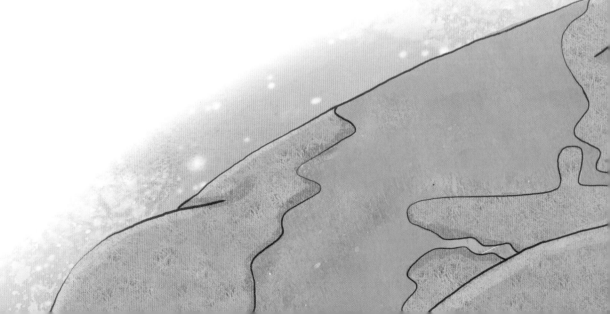

Ah! You are so great, and I am so small,
I hardly can think of you, World, at all;
And yet, when I said my prayers today,
My mother kissed me, and said, quite gay,

"If the wonderful world is great to you,
And great to Father and Mother, too,
You are more than the Earth, though you are such a dot!
You can love and think, and the Earth cannot!"

William Brighty Rands

Index of First Lines